SPORTING GESTURES

PUNCH
Plays the Game

Edited by William Hewison

A PUNCH BOOK

Published in association with

GRAFTON BOOKS

A Division of the Collins Publishing Group

Grafton Books
A Division of the Collins Publishing Group
8 Grafton Street, London W1X 3LA

Published by Grafton Books 1988

British Library Cataloguing in Publication Data
Sporting gestures: Punch plays the game.
1. English humorous cartoons – Collections
I. Hewison, William
741.5'942

ISBN 0-246-13400-3

Printed in Great Britain by William Collins Sons & Co. Ltd, Glasgow

Introduction

I've never forgotten the night-school psychologist who declared that cartoons reveal a heck of a lot about the cartoonists who produce them. Dangerous ground is psychology, a woolly-edged science if there ever was one, particularly in the hands of dabblers who get their half-baked notions from dog-eared paperbacks. This dabbler had it all worked out (with the help of that cross-talk duo Ego and Id) and was thus able to convince herself that she could see evidence of all kinds of weird, subconscious hang-ups lurking within the scratchy lines of any cartoon drawing. Psychology, no friend of Logic, can just about get away with murder. So, according to this lady, one cartoonist was a misogynist and another had unhealthy sexual urges. Marvellous, isn't it?

Now cartoons – or rather, a series of them from the same hand – do give us some tentative idea about what interests that particular cartoonist. Not daft presumptions that he was potty-trained too early, but indications that point towards certain activities. Comic artists, if they are to be any way successful, generally have to range over a wide area of subject-matter, but the regular reader need not be too perceptive in order to realise what they get up to when not slaving over a hot drawing-board. And a great number of them are interested in sport of one kind or another. Those who regularly swing a club on the municipal links or stand on the terraces cheering their home football team almost always give the game away through their drawings.

It's not that they stack their work with correct technical details; what demonstrates that a bloke knows what he is about is the fine-tuning of his joke ideas. Alex Graham, for instance, has squeezed a lot of comic mileage out of the fact that golf can become obsessional and addictive, a strong signal that he is well acquainted with the game at first hand. His enthusiast, golf-bag at the shoulder, who thumbs a lift to the golf course after wrecking his car against a tree, is a character we suspect is only slightly exaggerated.

Mind, it's unlikely that any of the artists here collected is a contender for the 100-metre Sprint or the Hop, Skip and Jump. There might be a lazy tennis player among them, or a careful ice skater. And if snooker can be thought of as a sport then I guess I could name five or six cartoonists who own no flashy waistcoats but are nifty at potting the red. Not many fox hunters among the fraternity these days, for sure, but I can vouch for several skilful fly-fishers, probably the best of whom is Merrily Harpur. Shootin'? Maybe at clay pigeons but not the proper stuff.

As for the rest, they manage quite well without personally engaging in any sport at all; these are the passive observers of the skiing slopes, the boxing ring, the running track, the tennis court – knowledgeable but non-doers, for ever on the look-out for some half-hidden facet which will activate another idea. So the hazards of the Olympic Winners' rostrum, the player/referee confrontations, the pre-match strategy conference with blackboard and attacking arrows, the advertising trade-marks on shirts, the radio commentators, the aggro on the terraces – all these are grist to the cartoonists' mill. Our pop psychologist would no doubt make a meal of that.

William Hewison
March 1988

"There's not much doing till 4.40!"

"You needn't bother . . . bad light stopped play."

*"Not **too** slow back, sir."*

"He's asked for political asylum."

"They don't use racquets any more."

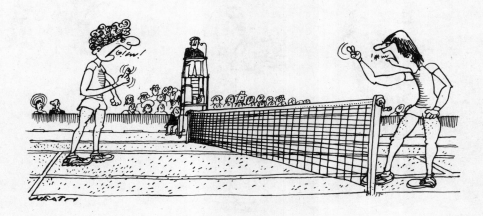

"…then you beat an egg into it…"

"Son, you're just going to have
to use your imagination and pretend
it's a video game."

"Always tell a foreigner – starts reading a newspaper from the front."

"There's still time to change your mind."

"Another world record! How can people see what he's advertising if he runs so fast?"

"Anyone got a spirit-level?"

"Steward's enquiry? What steward's enquiry?"

"He's unorthodox for a managing director, but he gets on well with the workers."

"Middle and leg, please!"

*"In our day you at least had to think there was severe provocation
before you got your retaliation in first!"*

"Do you really? What's your handicap?"

McLACHLAN

"He's a rotten player but he can't half advertise."

"That's another thing. I'm sick and tired of all this namby-pamby hugging and kissing every time one of them storms an enemy pill-box single-handed."

*"I just want to put back into the game of Rugby football a little of
what I've had out of it."*

"Excuse me, Sir, do you mind if we smoke?"

*"Of course their intelligence is carefully
bred out of them…"*

"If there's one thing I hate about a meet…"

"Disadvantage Brown."

"I hate to keep reminding you, but you've **tried** football, crime and show business."

"Of course, it's only really held together by the lettering."

"I hate to leave him – he was developing into a useful leg-spinner."

"Oh God!
Those frilly knickers!"

"It wouldn't have hurt him to miss the cricket for once!"

"…and a ball."

*"I suppose it had to happen –
Scottish tennis fans!"*

"*What was the word the doctor said I said while I was under the anaesthetic?*"

"Could you go over that bit again about lightning rapier-like thrusts to the very heart of their defence?"

"I never cease to be astonished at Lester's amazing will to win!."

"I'm going to call it football!"

*"Welcome to our club, sir! Mr Hoffmeyer here
will be happy to throw you around."*

"Good God! Sent off! Sometimes I wonder if Simpkins understands what this bloody war is all about."

"Pardon!"

*"I can't help getting emotional.
His father, his grandfather, and
his great-grandfather were all
sick in that corner."*

"Hold it a moment, Miss Forsyth. I've an idea I should be foot-faulting you."

"No skill? *You* try cutting an eye open, left-handed, wearing eight-ounce gloves."

"Just what the sport needed. An amnesty for Republican bullfighters still in hiding!"

"Well, I say one club's length from the
ball with a one stroke penalty."

"Just watch it, Shorty!"

"Hold it! Harry's got cramp!"

"What I want to see is a bit of senseless violence."

"I sometimes wonder if sponsorship isn't getting a little out of hand."

*"You should have consulted the committee before you accepted
the Snugfit Truss sponsorship, Major."*

"I'll never really understand British sportsmanship."

"Would you walk round with me while I announce tea and light refreshments now available in the Buffet car?"

"After the accident, it seemed a shame to waste the carton."

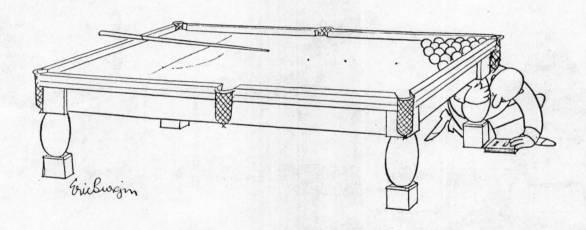

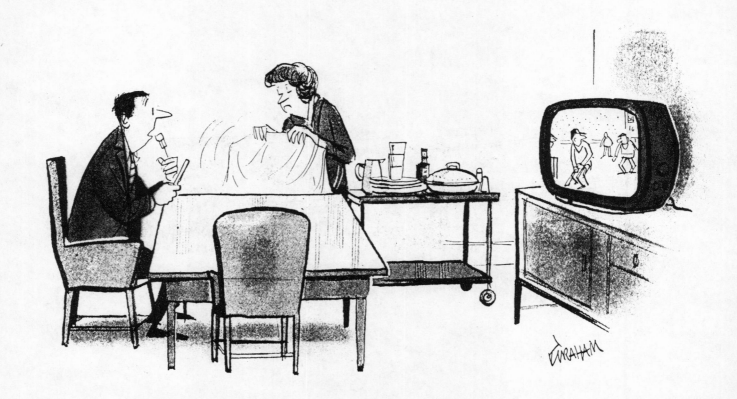

"Hogan seems pretty confident."

"Think, man! Is this hasty, dubious decision worth the risk of being held up to ridicule in front of millions by Jimmy Hill tonight?"

"His wife's divorcing him – he's probably working out how much she'll claim if he sinks it."

*"Which sportswear firm do
you want to be?"*

"Lord! I hope you win after all this practice."

"As a former captain of England and Loamshire, Tom, I think you would agree that it's fairly belting down."

"No one's actually ever bothered to climb the East Face before."

BANX

"I believe he owns a small newsagents in Battersea."

S. MCMURTRY.

"Strangely enough, he always felt pole-vaulting would conquer his vertigo."

"I got sent off."

*"There's never a shortage of rich widows fighting
for these chaps' attentions."*

"I don't mind the swatting – it's the bounce-bounce-bounce that gets on my nerves."

"The linesman, ref! How about consulting the linesman?"

"I still feel that the Olympics is no place for slow-bicycle racing."

"And if they start exchanging sweaters after the match, I'm resigning from MCC."

"Simmer down, Hayward – we all have days when we can't do a thing right."

"Howzat?"

*"Good Heavens! You really **were** killing a snake."*

"In view of the club's dire financial position, there will be a change of tactics this week!"

"It's no wonder we're an endangered species, really."

"At least consult your psychiatrist!"

"A furlong to go as I hand over to Peter O'Sullivan to work himself up into a frenzy for the finish."

"Cancelled? …the Darts Match?"

"Have you thought of taking out a personal injury policy?"

"I had hoped taking up a sport would get him out of the house a bit."

*"Try not to think too much about
what happened to the linesmen, Sir,
they know they're expendable."*

*"Me, I'd take a 5-iron, fade it slightly to the top
of the right-hand bunker, and let it roll gently down
the slope to within about a foot of the pin …"*

"Unfortunately, our country's just gone over to Fundamental Islam."

"I dare say someone will find a use for his inventions sooner or later."

*"Hello! When did **you** come in?"*

"*Hope this is over soon – I'm down to win the Women's Hammer-Throwing in the Olympics.*"

"I wish we had a few mid-field players with his flair."

"*I was rather hoping the local food would bring out the best in him.*"

"I think his sponsored days are numbered."

*"This new fly-half of yours –
what's his blood group?"*

*"Did you know that the
most popular sport in
Britain is buying
equipment?"*

"Come on, kid, you can do it. It's only a flat surface!"

"Come on, Sir! You can do it – another
two foot six inches and I've broken
the world record!"

"I told you those hours of early morning roadwork would pay off, kid."

"How do you like being on the board of directors, Wilkinson?"

"Frankly, Cleo, I'm more hurt than angry."

"Frankly, Henshaw, if gates go on falling like this, I can't see us *ever* finishing our paper on crowd hooliganism."

"I only wounded him but then my elephant trampled him to death."

"His concentration was upset by a sporting gesture on the part of his opponent in the third set."

"Well, Mr Kerslake, I strongly recommend you give up marathon running."

"In a word, you keep lobbing it up the middle in the hope that Ron will get a boot to it."

"Roy only plays really because it helps him with his business contacts."

"You've certainly got to hand it to these Manchester United supporters – they're game right to the end."

*"Thank God you brought the sponge, Wally –
he's got mud on his advertising!"*

*"It's a Spalding No. 7, but I don't think it's **my** Spalding No. 7."*

"It was his last request – he wanted his ashes thrown at the ref!"

"It's no use, Mr Goldberg – it just frightens the dogs!"

"…and sank the putt, so there I was needing a four for a seventy-nine."

"Motor racing been cancelled again?"

"World Cup, Test, Wimbledon — you'd think at least one of 'em would have the decency to pop a head in and say 'Thank you'."

"We had to introduce rugby league every fortnight!"

"Sex, sex, sex! That's all you ever think about!"

S.MCMURTRY.

"Hello, they're on the defensive – they've reverted to 4-4-2."

"Nice to see the old-fashioned winger back again, Fred."

"Damned weather! All right, Withers, start beating."

"You can't throw up now – we need the weight."